PSALMS

A PRAYER JOURNAL

LIFEWAY PRESS®

BRENTWOOD, TENNESSEE

ISBN: 978-1-0877-8851-7
Item: 005842865

To order additional copies of this resource, write to Lifeway Resources Customer Service; 200 Powell Place, Suite 100, Brentwood, TN 37027-7707; order online at lifeway.com; fax 615.251.5933; phone toll free 800.458.2772; or email orderentry@lifeway.com.

Printed in Dongguan, China

Lifeway Women Bible Studies
Lifeway Resources
200 Powell Place, Suite 100
Brentwood, TN 37027-7707

Lifeway Women Bible Studies

BECKY LOYD
director, Lifeway Women

TINA BOESCH
manager

CHELSEA WAACK
production leader

LAURA MAGNESS
content editor

ERIN FRANKLIN
production editor

LAUREN ERVIN
cover design

THIS JOURNAL BELONGS TO

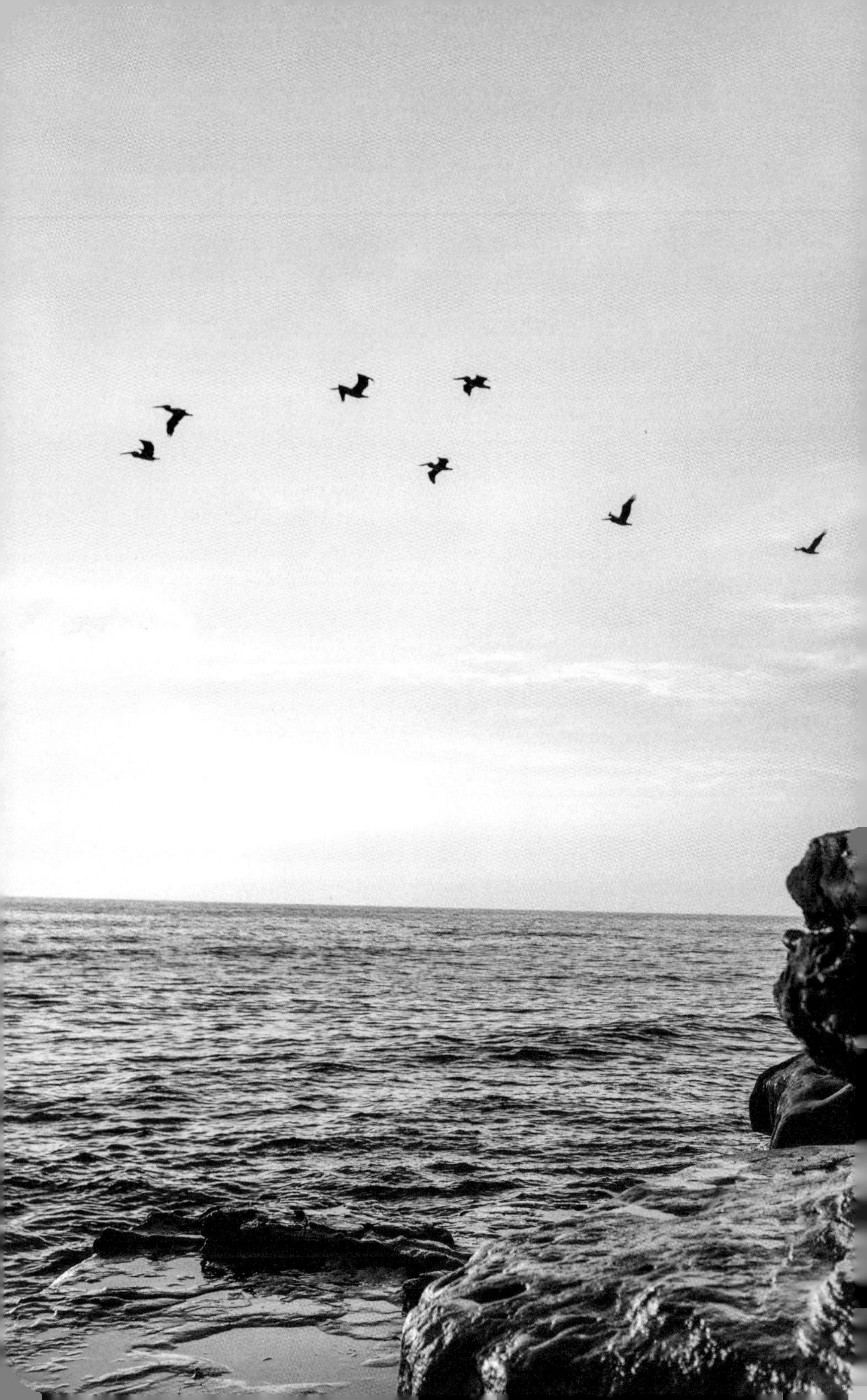

WELCOME!

We're so glad you have this journal in your hands and are taking this thirty-day prayer journey with us through Psalms.

The book of Psalms is itself a prayer journal—written prayers to God that range from songs of praise for His goodness and love to cries of lament and everything in-between. Spending time in this book draws our hearts closer to God and deepens our trust in Him. This journal is a tool that will help you do that by meditating on a variety of psalms and allowing them to inspire your own prayers.

This journal is divided into six weeks. Each week is tied to a genre of the psalms—thanksgiving, wisdom, lament, royalty, trust, and praise. These genres are described in more detail on the following pages. We've structured this journal so that you'll spend a week focusing your prayers on a specific theme.

In addition to the days of guided prayer, we've also included some Scripture memory challenges—opportunities for you to hide God's Word in your heart (Ps. 119:11)—as well as pages where you can write your own psalms as reflections on your days in prayer.

Our prayer for you is that through your time studying and imitating prayers of psalms, you'll grow closer to God and more comfortable in prayer.

Lifeway Women

ABOUT PSALMS

Background on the book of Psalms

Author

David is mentioned in the titles of seventy-three psalms. Twelve psalms are ascribed to Asaph and eleven to "the sons of Korah." Other named authors are Moses, Solomon, Heman, and Ethan. Fifty psalms are anonymous.

Date

The oldest psalm, Psalm 90, is that of Moses (1400s BC). The largest group was composed during the Davidic era (1010–970 BC). The final compilation probably occurred during the time of Ezra and Nehemiah (458–430 BC). Psalm 137 may have been the last psalm composed.

If you're interested in further study of Psalms, this journal has a companion Bible study, *As for Me: Life Through the Lens of the Psalms*. You can learn more and purchase the Bible study at lifeway.com/asforme.

Big Picture

The book of Psalms is part of a section of Old Testament books known as wisdom literature. Also included in this category are the books of Job, Proverbs, Ecclesiastes, and Song of Songs. Psalms is a collection of Hebrew poems and songs that focus on humanity's relationship with God and were recorded so they could be preserved as a part of Israel's worship practices. God, the true and glorious King, is worthy of all praise, thanksgiving, and confidence—whatever the occasion in personal or community life.[1]

ʼypes of Psalms

he psalms are traditionally categorized based on their main idea or writing style. raditionally, these categories include thanksgiving, wisdom, lament, kingship, trust, raise, prophecy, pilgrimage, and temple hymns. Many psalms fit into more than one f these categories.

.s you work your way through your prayer journal, you'll spend a week with each of the ɔllowing types of psalms.

ʼhanksgiving

hanksgiving psalms describe a situation of distress and how God delivered the psalmist. hese psalms show us our need to acknowledge God's work in our times of trouble and ɔ witness to others what God has done for us.

Visdom

/isdom psalms probe life's mysteries to teach the congregation about itself and God.

Kingship

ingship, or royalty, psalms detail the role of the human king in God's rule over His eople. They also point ahead to the Messiah, who would inaugurate God's kingdom.

,ament

salms of lament cry out for help in a situation of distress or frustration. Psalmists rotest their innocence or confess their sins. Such psalms show prayer as an honest ommunication with God in life's worst situations.

ʼrust

salms of trust are prayers or songs of praise that specifically highlight trust and onfidence in the Lord for who He is and how He has worked among His people.

ʼraise

salms of praise are hymns that lift the congregation's praise to God, describing God's reatness and majesty. In the hymn, worshipers invite one another to praise God and to rovide reasons for such praise.[2]

ɔotnotes:

Adapted from the CSB Lifeway Women's Bible (Nashville: Holman Bible Publishers, 2022), 749.

Types of psalms list adapted from *Holman Bible Dictionary* (Nashville: Holman Bible Publishers, 1991), accessed from logos.com (WORDsearch Corp., 2008).

Week One

THANKSGIVING

I will give you thanks with all my heart;
I will sing your praise before the heavenly beings.
I will bow down toward your holy temple
and give thanks to your name
for your constant love and truth.
You have exalted your name
and your promise above everything else.

. . .

If I walk into the thick of danger,
you will preserve my life
from the anger of my enemies.
You will extend your hand;
your right hand will save me.
The LORD will fulfill his purpose for me.
LORD, your faithful love endures forever;
do not abandon the work of your hands.

PSALM 138:1-2,7-8

date / /

Read Psalm 92. Reflect on the words in the psalm and journal your own prayers of thanksgiving to God.

date / /

Read Psalm 107. Reflect on the words in the psalm and journal your own prayers of thanksgiving to God.

Let them give thanks to the Lord for his faithful love and his wondrous works for all humanity.

PSALM 107:31

date / /

Read Psalm 116. Reflect on the words in the psalm and journal your own prayers of thanksgiving to God.

date / /

Read Psalm 118. Reflect on the words in the psalm and journal your own prayers of thanksgiving to God.

You are my God, and I will give you thanks. You are my God; I will exalt you. Give thanks to the LORD, for he is good; his faithful love endures forever.

PSALM 118:28-29

date / /

Read Psalm 138. Reflect on the words in the psalm and journal your own prayers of thanksgiving to God.

MY PSALM

Reflect on your prayers from this week and then turn them into a psalm.

Week Two

WISDOM

The instruction of the LORD is perfect,
renewing one's life;
the testimony of the LORD is trustworthy,
making the inexperienced wise.
The precepts of the LORD are right,
making the heart glad;
the command of the LORD is radiant,
making the eyes light up.
The fear of the LORD is pure,
enduring forever;
the ordinances of the LORD are reliable
and altogether righteous.
They are more desirable than gold—
than an abundance of pure gold;
and sweeter than honey
dripping from a honeycomb.

PSALM 19:7-10

date / /

Read Psalm 1. Reflect on the words in the psalm and journal your own prayers for godly wisdom.

His delight is in the LORD's instruction, and he meditates on it day and night.

PSALM 1:2

date / /

Read Psalm 19. Reflect on the words in the psalm and journal your own prayers for godly wisdom.

date / /

Read Psalm 37. Reflect on the words in the psalm and journal your own prayers for godly wisdom.

A person's steps are established by the LORD, and he takes pleasure in his way. Though he falls, he will not be overwhelmed, because the LORD supports him with his hand.

PSALM 37:23-24

date / /

Read Psalm 119:1-88. Reflect on the words in the psalm and journal your own prayers for godly wisdom.

date / /

Read Psalm 119:89-176. Reflect on the words in the psalm and journal your own prayers for godly wisdom.

MY PSALM

Reflect on your prayers from this week and then turn them into a psalm.

SCRIPTURE MEMORY CHALLENGE

Read this Scripture passage out loud three times.
Then, copy it onto a separate piece of paper.

But as for me,

LORD, my prayer to you

is for a time of favor.

In your abundant, faithful love,

God, answer me

with your sure salvation.

PSALM 69:13

SCRIPTURE MEMORY CHALLENGE

When you're ready, cover the left side of your journal.
Fill in the blanks with the missing words.

for me,

LORD, to you

is .

In your , faithful love,

God, me

with .

PSALM 69:13

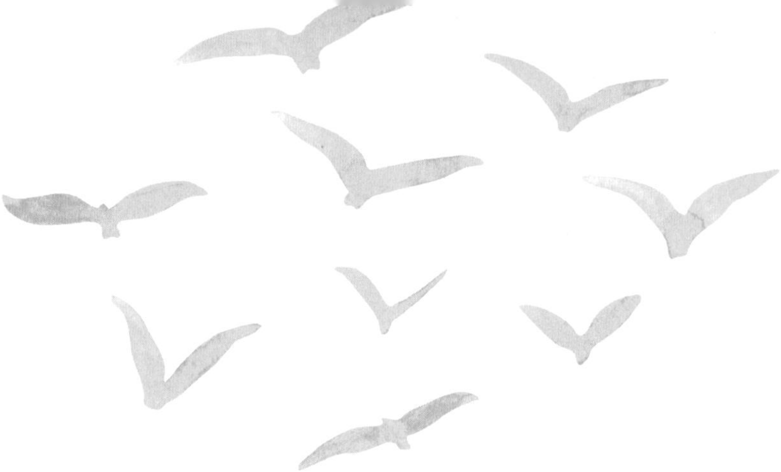

Week Three

KINGSHIP

The Lord reigns! He is robed in majesty;
the Lord is robed, enveloped in strength.
The world is firmly established;
it cannot be shaken.
Your throne has been established
from the beginning;
you are from eternity.
The floods have lifted up, Lord,
the floods have lifted up their voice;
the floods lift up their pounding waves.
Greater than the roar of a huge torrent—
the mighty breakers of the sea—
the Lord on high is majestic.
Lord, your testimonies are completely reliable;
holiness adorns your house
for all the days to come.

PSALM 93

date / /

Read Psalm 29. Reflect on the words in the psalm and journal your own prayers to God for His rule and reign.

date / /

Read Psalm 47. Reflect on the words in the psalm and journal your own prayers to God for His rule and reign.

Clap your hands, all you peoples; shout to God with a jubilant cry. For the LORD, the Most High, is awe-inspiring, a great King over the whole earth.

PSALM 47:1-2

date / /

Read Psalm 93. Reflect on the words in the psalm and journal your own prayers to God for His rule and reign.

date / /

Read Psalm 95. Reflect on the words in the psalm and journal your own prayers to God for His rule and reign.

Let's enter his presence with thanksgiving; let's shout triumphantly to him in song. For the LORD is a great God, a great King above all gods.

PSALM 95:2-3

date / /

Read Psalm 110. Reflect on the words in the psalm and journal your own prayers to God for His rule and reign.

MY PSALM

Reflect on your prayers from this week and then turn them into a psalm.

Week Four

LAMENT

As a deer longs for flowing streams,
so I long for you, God.
I thirst for God, the living God.
When can I come and appear before God?
My tears have been my food day and night,
while all day long people say to me,
"Where is your God?"
I remember this as I pour out my heart:
how I walked with many,
leading the festive procession to the house of God,
with joyful and thankful shouts.

. . .

The LORD will send his faithful love by day;
his song will be with me in the night—
a prayer to the God of my life.

PSALM 42:1-4,8

date / /

Read Psalm 3. Reflect on the words in the psalm and journal your own prayers of lament.

But you, Lord, are a shield around me, my glory, and the one who lifts up my head. I cry aloud to the Lord, and he answers me from his holy mountain.

PSALM 3:3-4

date / /

Read Psalm 27. Reflect on the words in the psalm and journal your own prayers of lament.

date / /

Read Psalm 42. Reflect on the words in the psalm and journal your own prayers of lament.

Why, my soul, are you so dejected? Why are you in such turmoil? Put your hope in God, for I will still praise him, my Savior and my God.

PSALM 42:5

date / /

Read Psalm 43. Reflect on the words in the psalm and journal your own prayers of lament.

date / /

Read Psalm 51. Reflect on the words in the psalm and journal your own prayers of lament.

MY PSALM

Reflect on your prayers from this week and then turn them into a psalm.

SCRIPTURE MEMORY CHALLENGE

Read this Scripture passage out loud three times.
Then, copy it onto a separate piece of paper.

But as for me,

God's presence is my good.

I have made the Lord God my refuge,

so I can tell about all you do.

PSALM 73:28

SCRIPTURE MEMORY CHALLENGE

When you're ready, cover the left side of your journal.
Fill in the blanks with the missing words.

But ________ ,

God's ________ is my good.

I have ________ ,

so I can tell about ________ .

PSALM 73:28

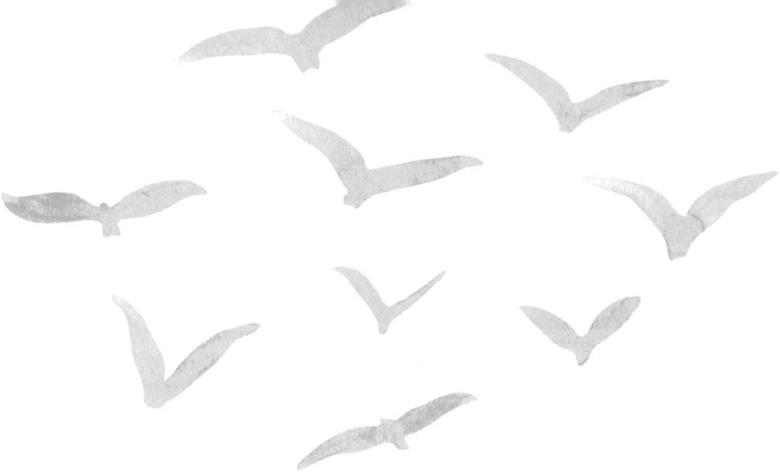

Week Five

TRUST

I lift my eyes toward the mountains.
Where will my help come from?
My help comes from the LORD,
the Maker of heaven and earth.
He will not allow your foot to slip;
your Protector will not slumber.
Indeed, the Protector of Israel
does not slumber or sleep.
The LORD protects you;
the LORD is a shelter right by your side.
The sun will not strike you by day
or the moon by night.
The LORD will protect you from all harm;
he will protect your life.
The LORD will protect your coming and going
both now and forever.

PSALM 121

date / /

Read Psalm 16. Reflect on the words in the psalm and journal your own prayers of trust in the Lord for who He is and how He is working.

date / /

Read Psalm 23. Reflect on the words in the psalm and journal your own prayers of trust in the Lord for who He is and how He is working.

The LORD is my shepherd; I have what I need.

PSALM 23:1

date / /

Read Psalm 63. Reflect on the words in the psalm and journal your own prayers of trust in the Lord for who He is and how He is working.

date / /

Read Psalm 91. Reflect on the words in the psalm and journal your own prayers of trust in the Lord for who He is and how He is working.

The one who lives under the protection of the Most High dwells in the shadow of the Almighty.

PSALM 91:1

date / /

Read Psalm 121. Reflect on the words in the psalm and journal your own prayers of trust in the Lord for who He is and how He is working.

MY PSALM

Reflect on your prayers from this week and then turn them into a psalm.

Week Six

PRAISE

Hallelujah!

Praise God in his sanctuary.

Praise him in his mighty expanse.

Praise him for his powerful acts;

praise him for his abundant greatness.

Praise him with the blast of a ram's horn;

praise him with harp and lyre.

Praise him with tambourine and dance;

praise him with strings and flute.

Praise him with resounding cymbals;

praise him with clashing cymbals.

Let everything that breathes praise the Lord.

Hallelujah!

PSALM 150

date / /

Read Psalm 8. Reflect on the words in the psalm and journal your own prayers of praise.

LORD, our Lord, how magnificent is your name throughout the earth! You have covered the heavens with your majesty.

PSALM 8:1

date / /

Read Psalm 103. Reflect on the words in the psalm and journal your own prayers of praise.

date / /

Read Psalm 111. Reflect on the words in the psalm and journal your own prayers of praise.

Hallelujah! I will praise the Lord with all my heart in the assembly of the upright and in the congregation.

PSALM 111:1

date / /

Read Psalm 145. Reflect on the words in the psalm and journal your own prayers of praise.

date / /

Read Psalm 150. Reflect on the words in the psalm and journal your own prayers of praise.

MY PSALM

Reflect on your prayers from this week and then turn them into a psalm.

SCRIPTURE MEMORY CHALLENGE

Read this Scripture passage out loud three times.
Then, copy it onto a separate piece of paper.

As for me,

I will tell about him forever;

I will sing praise

to the God of Jacob.

PSALM 75:9

SCRIPTURE MEMORY CHALLENGE

When you're ready, cover the left side of your journal.
Fill in the blanks with the missing words.

,

I will forever;

to the .

PSALM 75:9

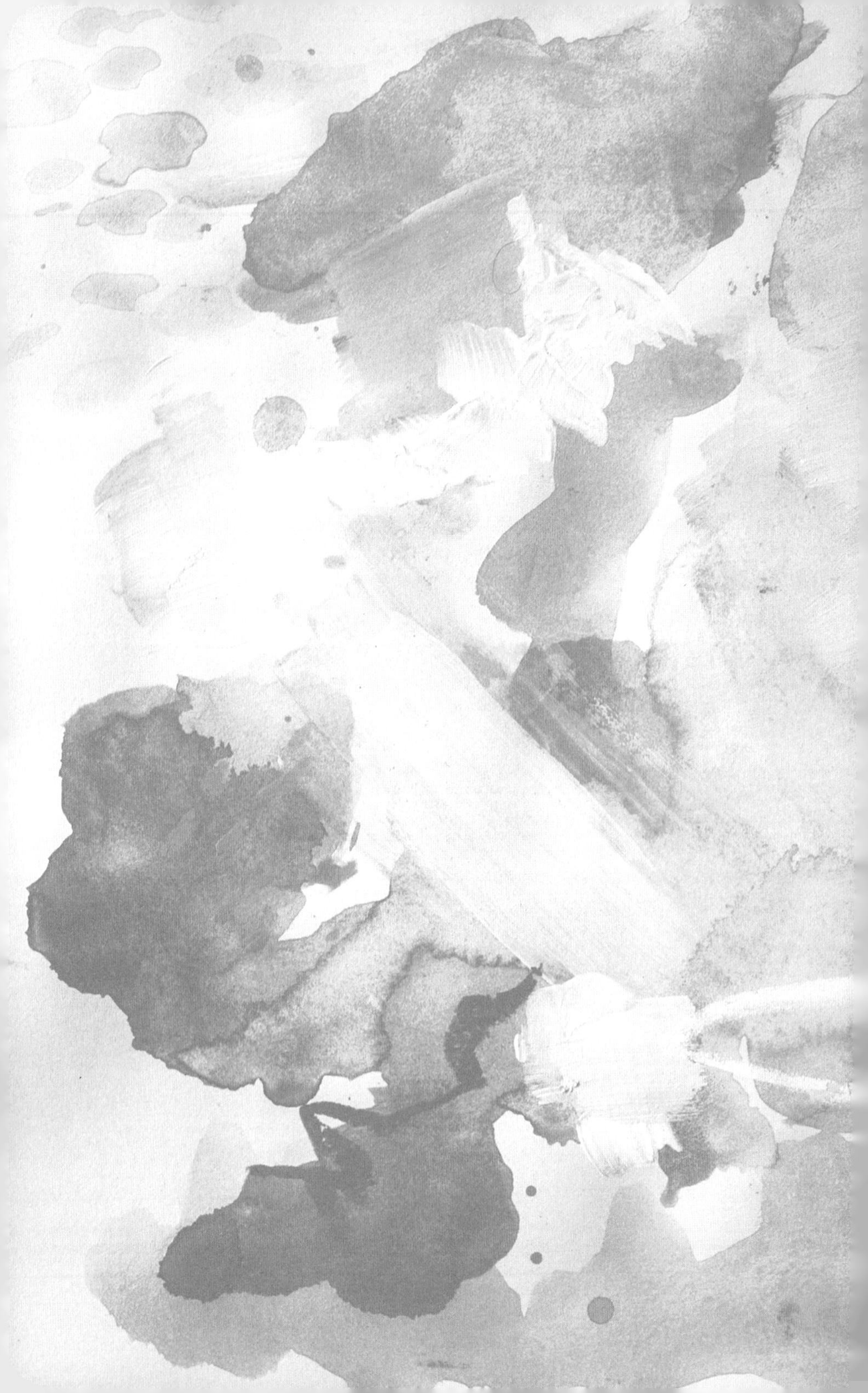

Looking to study Psalms?

Pick up recording artist Adrienne Camp's journey through the book of Psalms.

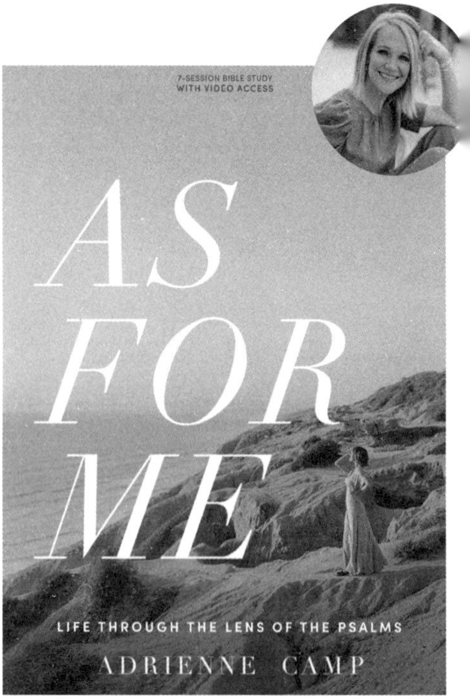

From songs of praise to cries of lament and everything in between, the book of Psalms captures the wide range of emotions in life. The psalmists paint a picture of a relationship with God that's filled with delays, disappointments, surprises, and triumphs. Through it all, their words model an incredible resolve to keep their eyes on God.

In this 7-session Bible study, gain a deeper understanding of who God is and be encouraged to hold onto Him no matter what's happening around you. Let the psalms become prayers you carry with you into every moment of every day, so that you too can say with confidence, "As for me, I will worship and serve the Lord no matter what."

Bible Study Book with Video Access 005839096 $20.99

Lifeway women

800.458.2772
Pricing and availability subject to change without notice.